*For all the children whose messages
and experiences helped me to write this book - AS*

*For all the children and young adults who helped inform
my illustrations with their life experiences - SA*

First published in Great Britain in 2021 by Otter-Barry Books,
Little Orchard, Burley Gate, Herefordshire, HR1 3QS
www.otterbarrybooks.com

ISBN 978-1-91307-460-9

Illustrated with pencil and Photoshop

Set in VAG Rundschrift D

Printed in China

9 8 7 6 5 4 3 2 1

YOU CAN!

Alexandra Strick • Steve Antony

Otter-Barry BOOKS

You can...

be brave,

be beautiful,

be clever,

be strong.

You can...

explore new worlds,

make amazing
discoveries,

love a good picture book
whatever your age,

do things together,

or alone.

You can...

discover what brings you happiness,

know it's OK to be sad or angry,

talk about how you feel.

You can...

dress up, paint your face, dance and be silly,

follow the crowd or...

lead the way,

dream BIG.

You can...

 overcome your fears,

challenge yourself,

surprise others,

surprise yourself,

do

things

you

couldn't

do

yesterday.

have fun practising something.

You can...

do something big

by doing something small,

inspire and encourage others,

stand up for what you believe in,

SAVE THE PLANET

make a difference.

You can...

know you have the right to be treated fairly,

the right to be listened to,

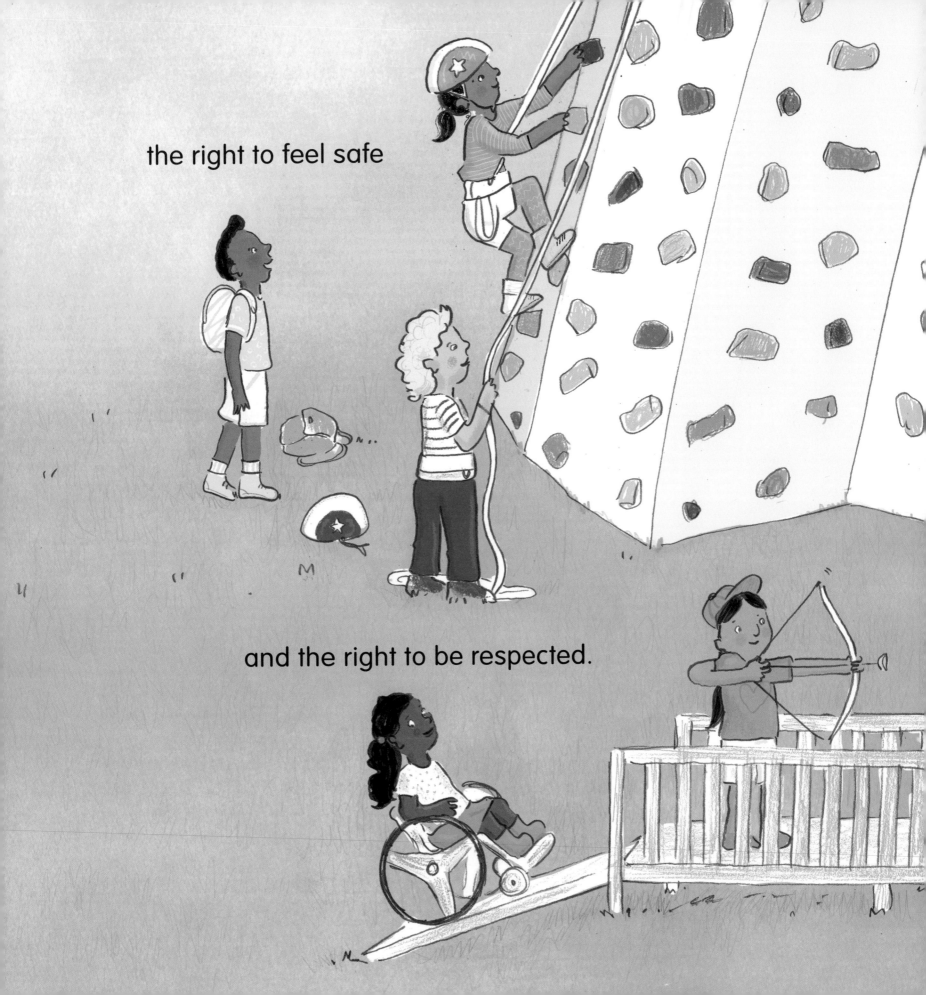

the right to feel safe

and the right to be respected.

You can...

push yourself,

do almost anything anyone else can do - even if you have to do it differently,

come first,

last,

or anywhere in between,

just give it a go.

You can...

find friendship

in surprising places,

be proud to be a
good friend,

be happy for others.

You can...

make new
resolutions

whenever you like,

make mistakes and learn from them,

forgive others

and yourself.

You can...

miss someone,

have bad days,

ask a grown-up for help,

share happy memories,

look forward to tomorrow.

You can...

be determined to
reach your goals,

refuse to be
put in a box,

find your own way,

support each other,

love and be loved.

You can...

believe in yourself,

be the best you can,

be kind,

be brilliant...

be YOU....

The story behind *You Can!*

This book is for children but it's also by children.

The book's author, Alexandra Strick, asked young people to tell her what they felt it was important to say in the text. So this book represents their messages to YOU.

The young contributors gave their ideas through meetings and video calls. To the right, you can see a picture of one of these meetings in action, with Alex and Steve!

They shared valuable words of advice and some of the useful things they wish they'd known when they were younger, to inspire and reassure, especially during tough times. They want to encourage you to stand up for what you believe, to find your own way, and also to know that you are enough — just as you are.

Steve Antony's wonderful illustrations show 14 imaginary characters growing up, page by page. To make sure that every reader can see themselves reflected in the pictures, Steve was also helped by Inclusive Minds and their brilliant team of young Inclusion Ambassadors.

A big thank you to everyone who helped us with the book! Alex and Steve x

To find out more about Inclusive Minds, go to www.inclusiveminds.com

Alexandra Strick

Zac

Ethan

Orla

Young Contributors on a video call with Alex and Steve